He's his old self, as any fool can
plainly see…Handsome…Debonair…
Immaculate…Irresistible…
England's own answer to Rock Hudson.
The one, the only,

ANDY CAPP

ANDY CAPP
SOUNDS OFF

by
Smythe

A FAWCETT GOLD MEDAL BOOK

Fawcett Publications, Inc., Greenwich, Conn.

Member of American Book Publishers Council, Inc.

THE REGULAR BARMAN USUALLY GIVES ME A FREE PINT TO GO SOMEWHERE ELSE...

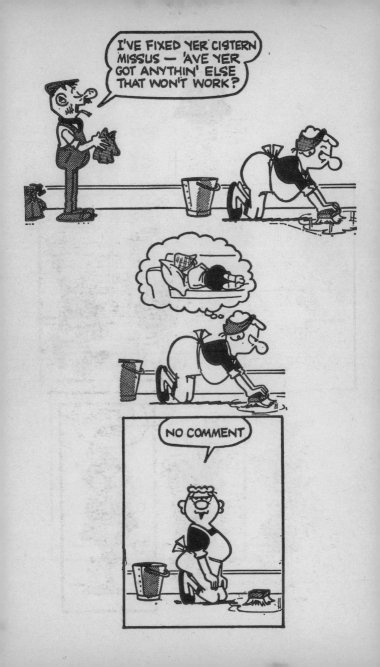

THREE O'CLOCK IN THE MORNIN'! — WHAT'S THE EXCUSE *THIS* TIME?

WE WERE PLAYIN' RUSSIA...THERE!

THAT SOUNDS REASONABLE...

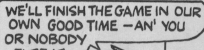

'E SNORED ALL THE TIME I WAS TALKIN'! — DID YER 'EAR 'IM, PET?

I DID THAT — 'E WOKE ME UP!

NOW WHAT 'AVE I SAID?

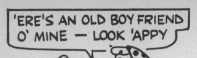

WALKIN' UP THE ROAD I WAS JUST THINKIN' 'OW MANY YEARS I'VE BIN COMIN' IN 'ERE —

LABOUR EXCHANGE

WHAT YER AFTER, MATE — A *RAISE*? HEH! HEH!

?

'OW DID YER KNOW?

SHRIEK

THIS IS RIDICULOUS, PET- FANCY US FIGHTIN' OVER ANYTHIN' AS IDIOTIC AS YOUR FAMILY

68-6-4